Set design by Dean Holzman *Photo by George Byron Griffiths*

Barbara June Patterson in a scene from the Illusion Theater production of *Murderers*.

MURDERERS

BY JEFFREY HATCHER

★

★

DRAMATISTS
PLAY SERVICE
INC.

MURDERERS was first produced by Illusion Theater, Minneapolis, Minnesota, Michael H. Robbins and Bonnie Morris, Producing Directors.

For Elizabeth Holmberg Stevens
"Toots"

AUTHOR'S NOTE

Murderers consists of three monologues and was designed to be performed on a bare stage. When the opening monologue, "The Man Who Married His Mother-in-Law," was first presented, I played the character. It was at the Minnesota Fringe Festival, and because we had only thirty minutes to do the show and pack away the set before the next act came in, all we could manage in the way of design were six light cues, an office chair, intro and outro music, and my tuxedo. When I added the companion pieces "Margaret Faydle Comes to Town" and "Match Wits with Minka Lupino" at Illusion Theater's Fresh Ink Series, we were again under time and design constraints. As before, we went with only a handful of cues and left it to the performers, Phyllis Wright and Barbara June Patterson, to do their magic.

When all three monologues were finally put together for the premiere of *Murderers* at Illusion, the director, Sarah Gioia, figured we shouldn't screw around with what had worked so well before. So, despite a sizeable budget this time and three terrific actors — Phyllis, Barbara June and Bob Davis in the role I had performed — we kept things simple, and the show was a hit. So, I lean towards productions of *Murderers* that have simple sets for simple set changes, tight cues, brief (seconds) changeovers from one monologue to another, and a running time that is somewhere between 90 and 100 minutes.

Get 'em in, get 'em out, and my apologies to the folks who run the refreshment bar.

—Jeff Hatcher

MURDERERS was commissioned by and premiered at Illusion Theater (Michael H. Robins and Bonnie Morris, Producing Directors), in Minneapolis, Minnesota, in February 2005. It was directed by Sarah Gioia; the set design was by Dean Holzman; and the stage manager was Matthew Dawson. The cast was as follows:

GERALD .... Bob Davis
LUCY .... Barbara June Patterson
MINKA .... Phyllis Wright

MURDERERS was subsequently produced by Philadelphia Theatre Company, (Sara Garonzik, Producing Artistic Director) in Philadelphia, Pennsylvania, opening on October 11, 2006. It was directed by Michael Bush; the set design was by Jim Noone; the lighting design was by Traci Klainer; the costume design was by Karen Ann Ledger; and the sound design and original music were by Ryan Rumery. The cast was as follows:

GERALD .... Brent Langdon
LUCY .... Marylouise Burke
MINKA .... Kristine Nielsen

CHARACTERS

MURDERERS consists of three monologues:

"THE MAN WHO MARRIED HIS MOTHER-IN-LAW"

GERALD HALVERSON, a dapper man in his late 30s, early 40s. He wears a beautifully cut black tuxedo.

"MARGARET FAYDLE COMES TO TOWN"

LUCY STICKLER, a pert, adorable housewife in her 70s. She wears clothing appropriate to her age and personality.

"MATCH WITS WITH MINKA LUPINO"

MINKA LUPINO, a very pleasant woman in her 40s. She wears a professional-looking suit with black skirt and splashy-colored jacket.

PLACE

Riddle Key, Florida — a retirement community.

TIME

Now.

MURDERERS

At the start of the play, Gerald, Lucy, and Minka are discovered in three pools of light, staring out front, a la "To Tell the Truth."

GERALD. I am a murderer.
LUCY. I am a murderer.
MINKA. I am a murderer. *(They look at each other, as if waiting for one of them to go first. Then Lucy and Minka exit. And Gerald begins …)*

THE MAN WHO MARRIED HIS MOTHER-IN-LAW

GERALD. I am a murderer.

This is my uniform.

All the best murderers wear black tie when committing murder. *Sleuth. Dial "M" For Murder.* Various episodes of *Columbo.* Murder mysteries teach us that. Murder mysteries also teach us that the best murderers always make a fatal mistake. The unforeseen circumstance. The overlooked detail. The character flaw that unravels the whole, perfect, orchestrated plot.

Spiff used to say one should always wear black tie for formal occasions. I should think a murder would qualify.

None of us had any inkling of Spiffy's illness until well after the party for Puss and Peppar. Puss and Spiffy had known each other since they were three years old, and Puss's new husband, Peppar, a "character," a plaid cummerbund, lampshade at parties type who'd been married and widowed twice already, was now taking his new bride away, from the snows of the North to the shores of Florida.

The farewell party is marvelous! That's one of Spiff's words:

marvelous! A debutante's word from the forties. Spiff was one of those "gals" who studied *Vogue* for a living and never settled for that aging Vassar-hairband look. Spiff is a widow herself. Her husband died fifteen years ago. Tonight she is wearing one of her ultra-suede pant suits with the Nehru tunic and military buttons. She looks like Diana Vreeland's idea of "Dr. No."

Ting ting ting ting! Spiff is making a toast.

"Those of you who can still raise your arms above your chests, please take up a glass. It is hard to find one love of your life, let alone a second. Puss, you and Peppar are truly blessed. Bon voyage!"

Here, here, clink-clink. Drink.

The next day Puss and Peppar flew down to Florida. Three weeks later Puss was dead.

She'd gotten a cold that turned into pneumonia and then her respirator gave out.

Peppar called Spiff with the news: "Puss was in such pain. It was better this way. I'm gonna move to Arizona."

Spiff took Puss's death well and didn't want to discuss the details. When people die, Spiff takes it, marks it, and moves on.

Laura takes a dim view of this. "Mom has never shown much emotion about anyone's death. I think that's horrible."

Laura thinks one should work harder to get to the grief that you then have to work harder to get out of.

Spiff never knows what to call me: son-in-law, daughter's boyfriend, live-in lover …

Laura and I are not married. We met fifteen years ago in college outside Washington, D.C., in West Virginia of all places, lived there together for seven years, so I joke with Spiff that we're probably a common-law couple anyway. Spiff loves us, but our unmarried status irritates her. It's impractical. And she is nothing if not a highly practical woman. As you shall see.

The first inkling of her illness came in February. Her appetite was poor. She had been tired a lot. Laura took her to Dr. Rosenblum for some tests. A few days later, he called and said we should all come in.

"Spiff. It's your kidneys. You have ninety percent failure. You have six, eight weeks at the most."

As we left the office, Spiff marches to the elevator and presses the up button.

Laura looks at me, "Mom, we're going down, not up."

Spiff snaps: "Up is where my lawyers are."

She had made the appointment in advance.

In the lawyer's office, we sit down with the estates attorney, Arthur Adelot, which sounds like a mnemonic, but is actually his name. Arthur is a man whose discretion is so discreet it is not even noticed.

Adelot is holding a print-out.

"Your estate as of this morning is estimated at approximately five million dollars, give or take."

Spiff nods. "And what happens to it if I die today?"

"Well, your heir is your daughter, Laura and her … boyfriend, yes? Well, the Feds, for your bracket, take forty percent. Forty percent of five million is two million, leaving three million."

Spiff nods. "Three million. Not bad."

"Well, it's not so simple as that. You see, you don't have the two million in cash. You'd have to sell stock. Your stocks are very old. Heirs will have to pay capital gains. That's another third. Now you're down to two million. Sell the house, there's more capital gain, now you're under one million five."

Spiffy gives us a dirty look: "All those years you kept trying to make me vote Democratic. Isn't there any way around this goddamn mess!?"

This is the first emotion I have seen Spiffy reveal so far. And it has not been about her pending death. It is about her pending death *tax*.

Adelot shakes his head: "The only sheltered arrangement the Feds recognize is that between a husband and his wife. A spouse may leave any amount to the remaining spouse, and the IRS can't touch a penny of it."

Now, I cannot tell you that it was *much* later that the plan struck me …

… because it struck me immediately.

The only question was: how to bring it up.

That night, over dinner at the club, I gin up my courage to speak when Spiff suddenly looks across the table and says:

"I think we should get married."

Laura looks up. "Who?"

"Arthur said a spouse could leave any amount to the remaining spouse without paying a penny in taxes. I think Gerald and I should get married, so that when I die, you two can inherit my estate without having to pay the goddamn government. I have two months. That's plenty of time to do all the official things, and then … when I'm gone … you two get everything."

There is a requisite stunned silence. Laura is *actually* stunned, I'm requisite.

"Now, we couldn't get married here. I wouldn't want anyone to know. Not for my sake, I'm going to be dead, but for Laura's."

Laura sputters. "Mother, this is ridiculous! My husband is not marrying my mother!"

"Honey, he's not your husband. You know I think Gerald is marvelous, but he's never going to make much money. Nor will you. You've practically been living off me for years!"

Spiff actually likes me a lot, but she is not blind to the fact that I'm a ne'er-do-well who's never going to keep her daughter in the manner to which Spiff thinks she should be accustomed.

I am aching to turn to Laura and say, "She's right, you know." After all, Spiff has come up with the same plan as I. But the best thing is for Laura to come to the decision by herself, on her own.

It comes that night. After the drive home in our Toyota, as we pass the BMWs and the Jaguars driven by people far less deserving, interesting and ironic as we. It comes at the apartment that night. The is it funky? Are we bohemian? Aren't we a little old for this kind of life? apartment we've been living in for ten years; lying under the covers, staring at the stain in the ceiling, not speaking a word until Laura says, "Where would you have to go to get married?"

Florida. The Riddle Key Luxury Senior Retirement Living Center and Golf Course.

Riddle Key is one of those upscale, gated, waterfront developments that caters to "seasoned citizens." "Seasoned." Like we're going to eat them. For five hundred thousand dollars, Riddle Key provides you with a two-bedroom luxury villa with a five-year lease. You're betting you don't die before year five or after year five. They're betting you die … well, they're just betting you die. A surprising number of people die on the fifth anniversary exactly. The Greatest Generation is nothing if not prompt.

Dr. Rosenblum has given Spiff a month, two at the outside, so we are able to negotiate a less onerous lease plan. After we arrive in Florida and marry at a justice of the peace, we settle in and wait it out. I keep a diary with notes and observations:

Week One. I did not know Bob Barker's hair was white. I am not usually up by eleven most days, but now eleven is lunch time. Call Laura every day. Dinners are pretty basic. Lean Cuisines mostly. Note to self: Brillo pads cost more than I would have imagined.

Week Two. *The Young and the Restless* is actually a pretty good show. No sign yet of physical deterioration in Spiff. Call Laura every *other* day. She has moved from our apartment into Spiff's house. Which surprises me. But it is practical. Went out to dinner once this week. Everyone eats at five P.M. and goes to bed before sundown. It's like living at the Antarctic.

Week Three. Naps are good. Spiff holding up well, so went to dinner three times this week and out to lunch twice. Talked to Laura Sunday. She's bought a new car. A Jaguar with a voice activated phone and satellite directional system. Laura is getting used to her new status.

Week Four. A knock at the door.

This is the first this has happened. Spiff and I look at each other as if G-men have come to arrest us.

When I open the door I see standing on the threshold a strange mirror image of ourselves. An old woman, like Spiff but older, and a man, like me but ... weirder. She's a blue rinse number in a lavender silk pantsuit with lots of jewelry. He's in his fifties, but his hair is blonde, Rumplestiltskin gold.

"Hi. Jerry Waldenow."

"And I'm Shirl. We live in the condo across the street, seen you come in and out. We're going to dinner. Would you like to join us?"

I am about to politely decline, when I hear Spiff say:

"That would be *marvelous.*"

We go to dinner at the Blue Hair Café, which is the first evidence I've seen of irony in Florida. Shirl is eighty-seven years old, formerly of Riverdale in the Bronx. Husband Irving was very successful in the flooring business. He died three years ago soon after they came down to Riddle Key.

Shirl sniffs, takes Jerry's hand. "I met Jerry on a cruise. And it's been bliss ever since."

Jerry is more than thirty years younger than Shirl. With his double-breasted blue blazer and orange ascot, he looks like a kid's version of a sophisticate, circa 1973. I don't think he is with Shirl or indeed *any* woman for "the physical part," though I get the idea from Shirl's comments that he "performs well." Shirl is open about such things.

Spiff is open about her illness, about how long she's got. Shirl and Jerry are very sympathetic. When the evening is over and we're back at Riddle Key — Shirl calling out so all the burglars can hear, "Visit anytime, the garage door's always open!" — I say to Spiff: "Can you believe it? He's a gigolo."

Spiff surprises me.

"Oh, who cares if he's a gigolo? He doesn't have to be with an eighty-seven-year-old women. I'm sure he could be with a seventy-seven-year-old woman. It's money well spent."

"So you grant he's only in it for the money."

"Unlike…?"

I start to stammer, unable to defend myself.

Spiff rescues me. She pats my cheek.

"Don't get all worked up. Our children get so righteous when it comes to sex and money."

Week Six. Spiff is gaining weight. She'd lost fifteen pounds up north, but now she's gaining. Her "Dr. No" outfits don't fit anymore. I suggest we see a physician.

Spiff says, "Isn't my dying the whole idea?"

She has a point, but I convince her to make an appointment with the onsite physician, Dr. Nagangupta. We have had her medical records sent from home.

Says Dr. Nagangupta: "I would like to run a few tests of my own."

As we leave the office we see Shirl and Jerry pull up in a 1965 red convertible Mustang. Would we like to join them for nine holes?

Jerry says: "You gotta work on your tan, Ger."

I realize suddenly we have the same name. Gerald and Jerry. He's my gay, suntanned gigolo doppelganger.

I start to politely decline when I hear:

"That would be *marvelous!*"

Nine holes. Which for someone like me is like the opening of *Saving Private Ryan.*

Spiff and Shirl tease me about my gasping, my sweating, my calling for medics.

At that precise moment a voice calls out: "SPIFF!"

We turn from the hole to see a small, wizened man has made his way to the putting green.

"Peppar! What the hell are you doing here?"

Peppar toddles up in his golf togs. "I came back. I did not like all the young people in Arizona."

Peppar looks at me. He can't place me. I'm out of context.

Spiff stumbles through the introductions. "Peppar, this is Shirley, Jerry, and this is my … this is Gerald, you remember you met him at the party for you and Puss."

Peppar has tears in his eyes.

"Y'know, Spiff, it was good Puss went like she did. She was in such pain. My first two wives too. Such pain." There is a moment of silence. Then Peppar claps his hands. "Hey, Spiff, how about we cut the rug? There's a Big Band Swing Dance at the club Saturday night! We could all go! You me, Shirl and Jerry!"

I have been left out.

Jerry leaps in. "What about Gerald?"

Peppar squints at me. "You wanna come with us old folk? Wouldn't you rather be off at one of your protest meetings or hootenannies?"

Spiff takes my hand. "You've been cooped up with me for weeks. Besides, it's a formal affair, and you don't own a dinner jacket. Take Saturday night off, have a night on the town."

Peppar says, "Yeah, you can go hang out with your Smothers Brothers and your Timothy Learys."

When we get back to the condo, the fight commences.

"I don't want you going out with Peppar!"

"What do you think is going to happen? Peppar's almost ninety. The last time we ate together I had to cut his meat."

"How would you feel if I went out on a date?"

"I don't think someone would like that."

"Ha. I didn't think you would."

"I mean: Laura."

There is no possible response I can make that will salvage me. But Spiff does. She comes to me, puts a hand on my cheek, smiling, forgiving whatever sin there is.

I stare into her eyes.

I see her at her debut, at a dance fifty years ago. In the back of a car, in a rumble seat, bathtub gin and a cigarette in the wind. The smell of lilacs breezing over a country club veranda as she closes her eyes and tilts back her head for her first kiss.

I lean towards Spiff. The tiniest movement.

She turns.

She goes off to her bedroom and flicks on the TV. *Murder She*

Wrote is on.

This is Monday night. The dance is Saturday. The next days' diary entries go like this:

Tuesday: Spiff goes to a dress shop and buys what I would consider a very revealing black dress.

Wednesday: Spiff gets a hairdo, a manicure and a pedicure.

Thursday: Spiff buys a pair of evening shoes. The shoes are not open toed. So, I ask you: What was the pedicure for? At what point in the evening does she intend to be wearing no shoes and showing her toes?

That afternoon I go out to take a walk along the docks. As I pass the clinic, Dr. Nagangupta waves me inside.

"I have back your wife's tests."

I nod, "Doctor, we know the diag — "

"The diagnosis you had is very wrong. It is in fact completely incorrect. Where your Doctor Rosenblum has her with ninety percent kidney failure, he has misread the chart. It is *nineteen* percent kidney failure."

"But what about the weakness? The sleeping?"

"Oh, she has kidney trouble, yes, but it can be addressed through dialysis along with diet and medication."

"But her gaining weight. Isn't that bad?"

"No! Her appetite is back! We have many fine restaurants in Riddle Key. I tell you this first because I think good news should come from loved ones. Don't you?"

"Doctor, what will happen if she doesn't receive treatment, dialysis?"

"Well, you must start dialysis immediately. Without that, a few months, one, maybe, two, she'll die."

I started back to the condo. I tried to think. I should tell Spiff immediately, tell her the good news.

Instead I call Laura.

Laura does not answer. The architect answers. He's doing drawings for the new addition. Laura has gone away for the weekend. To a spa. Says the architect: "Oop. Gotta go. Pool contractor's here."

So I do not tell Spiff the news. I do not tell her that night. Or the next morning or the day after that.

On the third day, Saturday, I wake early and head down to the man-made lagoon to take a walk, clear my head, when Jerry's red Mustang comes into view.

"Gerald! Got a minute?"

He gets out of the car and we stand at the edge of the "ocean."

"Shirl slipped in the garage last night. Broke her hip. They did an X-ray. Bone cancer, terminal, she's in the hospital now. Guess I'll have to go to the dance alone tonight. But that's not what I wanted to talk to you about. See, it was Dr. Nagangupta who treated her. He said, 'I wish it was good news I was telling you ... like Mr. Halverson.'"

I swallow.

"Have you told Spiff her good news?"

I hesitate.

"You're hesitating. You're thinking of lying to me. I've just been chatting with Spiff in the backyard and she reiterated that she only has a matter of weeks. You know what I think? I think Gerald's being a naughty gigolo. I think Gerald's hoping Spiff kicks it sooner rather than later. Am I right?"

"What do you want?"

"Half of everything you'll get. You can start now. Ten thousand a month."

"What if I go right back now and tell Spiff the truth?"

"Three days late? I get Nagangupta to tell Spiff that he told you the good news three days ago, Spiff's gonna wonder why her loving husband waited three days to tell her."

I look like I'm trying to decide.

"Ten thousand. I'll give you a check tonight. After the dance."

"Goody. *Ciao,* fella!"

His convertible zooms away, the exhaust fumes trailing his wake.

It would have to be tonight. The dance begins at six P.M.

Ten A.M. When I get back, Spiff is taking a shower. I go into the utility room and find bleach and ammonia. From the kitchen, I get a large plastic baggie.

Noon. Take a quick trip into Sarasota to a beauty salon to get some supplies. Pay in cash.

One P.M. Stop at a hardware store. Buy a large sponge and a pair of yellow rubber gloves. Pay in cash.

Two P.M. Stop at a clothing store and a bookstore. Buy certain essentials for the evening. Cash.

Four P.M. Back at the condo. Spiff is taking her nap. I check the book I've bought for information on toxins and the respiratory system.

Five o'clock. Spiffy is dressed and ready when the doorbell rings.

Peppar is here.

"Hey, fella. Not smokin' any of that ganja reefer, I hope!"

I fix Spiff and Peppar a couple of drinks. I check my watch. 5:43. When I look up Spiff is staring at me.

"Gerald? You look so forlorn. Why don't you come with us? Peppar won't mind, would you, Pep?"

I shake my head. I say:

"I didn't bring dinner clothes. You said one should always wear black tie for formal occasions."

Spiff takes my hand. "Sweetie ... in your case ... I'd make an exception."

"Aw, don't beg him, Spiff," says Peppar, "he'd feel funny out there without his disco pants and his moccasins."

Before Spiff is out the door, she suddenly comes round and kisses me. Not quite the cheek, not quite the lips. But inside the range of impropriety.

Once Peppar's Lincoln has pulled away, I go into gear.

First to my bedroom to get the new tux I've bought. Spiff hasn't seen it, so that was fairly easy to get away with.

Then in the bathroom, I get out the blonde wig from the beauty salon. A clip here and a snip there and I fit it on my head. From a distance, it will do.

I pour the bleach and the ammonia into the baggie, then let the sponge soak up the concoction. I seal the bag. I get the rubber gloves.

I walk evenly across the street. If anyone sees me going from my house to his — dog walkers, the Cuban gardeners, roaming senility cases — they'll think I'm him. And if anyone asks what he was doing at my house, I'll tell them he came over for a drink. He was despondent.

The garage door is always open, Shirl said. And it is.

There, inside, is the Mustang. Candy red, the white top down.

I hear a sound at the door to the kitchen. I back behind the garbage can and put on the rubber gloves. The door opens and there he is. In a tux. Like mine. Hair like mine. I open the baggie.

He gets in behind the wheel. He slips the key into the ignition.

And the sponge goes around his face. His arms flail a moment, I dodge his nails. Then he slumps. Five seconds. The sponge goes back into the baggie.

Inside, I get towels and stuff them under the garage doors.

I take Jerry's fingers, place them on the key and turn the ignition.

The V-8 motor roars. And the exhaust pours out of the pipe. A car that vintage with a V-8 engine, he should be dead in twenty minutes.

I leave the way I came.

Once back in our condo, I incinerate the sponge, the wig, the gloves on the patio grill.

And then … I rehearse my speech. I will call Laura. And I will tell her I am not coming back. I will explain as best I can. But I must save my strength and courage and I daresay eloquence … for Spiff.

I must tell her about Dr. Nagangupta's diagnosis.

I must convince her of the treatment that will add years to her life.

And I must persuade her to make our marriage real.

I have realized — as far back as the moment Jerry told me he planned to blackmail me — that what I feared was not the loss of five million dollars. It was the loss of her.

It's just past eight when I hear the sirens.

I peek through the front curtains. The sirens are getting closer. I can see the reflection of the red and blue lights in the palm trees.

Then I see the ambulance.

It zooms around the corner, down the street towards Jerry's house.

And then … it zooms by.

I watch as the lights go around the curve and up, up the street … to the club.

By the time I reach the clubhouse, I see the crowd gathered at the door to the ballroom.

Inside, Peppar kneels on the parquet.

On the floor is Spiff, on her back, an oxygen mask over her face. Medics are working on her.

As we rush into the hospital, Pepper tries to explain.

"We were dancing and she was laughing and then she just went down like a sack of tomatoes."

I tell the nurse who I am. "I am her husband."

She tries not to react to this, says they're checking for everything, heart, stroke.

I tell them: "Her kidneys are in end-stage renal failure."

The nurse asks: "Is she taking medication, on dialysis?"

"No."

She stares at me. "She's not under treatment?"

" … No."

The nurse picks up the phone. "Who is your doctor?"

"Our doctor?"

"Sir, who is your doctor and when did your wife last see him?"

I open my mouth to answer … but I am saved by Spiff. They're bringing her into ICU on a stretcher. Her face has a grimace on it.

Peppar groans: "She is in such pain."

The nurse says: "She's been asking for her husband."

A rush of warmth comes over me. Then I think — "*Which* husband did she ask for?"

I go into the room. The whoosh of the respirator, the beep of the heart monitor crowd my thoughts.

Someone taps my shoulder. "A gentleman wants to see you."

In the hall is a little, bald man with a … police badge.

"Sergeant Padilla. I am sorry about your wife. Hope everything works out. May I speak to you a moment?"

"Certainly, Sergeant."

"There was a death on your street this evening. Mr. Jerry Waldenow. Exhaust fumes, very old car. But pretty. I wanted to ask was there anything you might have noticed about him recently, anything peculiar…?"

"No. No. Well. Well … he *did* tell me … he told me *recently* … actually … that his wife was very ill. Terminal. He seemed despondent."

"Despondent. I see. Well, of course we have to treat it as any mysterious death. See if we find some knock-out drug in his system or a bonk on the head, a bruise."

I think to myself, "You won't find drugs and you won't find a bruise."

"Still I bet we come out with suicide."

When Sergeant Padilla is gone I go back into the ICU room. Peppar has tottered off somewhere.

It's so quiet in there.

I take her hand. I look at the wedding ring her first husband gave her. I never gave her a ring. I'll correct that. I'll get it right this time.

Then I notice something. *Why* is it so quiet? No whoosh. No beep. Then a sound begins. I look at the monitor next to the bed. The green line, the flat … I look down. The plug on the respirator! I go to the floor. I try to stick it back in …

That's when the doctors and the nurses rush into the room and see me. On the floor, with the plug in my hand.

Sergeant Padilla gets the case. He speaks to Dr. Nagangupta,

Laura, the doctors and lawyers. I make a show of protest, but I am not convincing, so I am convicted.

First-degree murder. Death penalty.

Laura does not speak to me again. Ever. But her representative does. Arthur Adelot. He has news.

"According to your mother-in-law's new will, you are the beneficiary of her entire estate. But since you're about to die … "

"Naturally I will leave the entire five million to Laura."

"Well. It's not that simple. You met Laura in college, yes?"

"Yes."

"Lived in West Virginia for seven years, yes?"

" … Yes…?"

"West Virginia has common-law marriage. According to West Virginia law you were legally married. To Laura. So when you attempted to marry her mother in Florida you were committing bigamy, and hence the will is invalid. Which means the estate will go into probate, which means years, attorney's fees, forty percent, capital gains, lose the house. Laura will be lucky to walk away with less than a million. Just thought you should know."

I never got another visitor … except one.

Peppar came. Week before the execution.

The fan was blowing in the visitor's room

He said: "I understand. Spiff was in such pain. It was the same with Puss. And my first two wives. They were in such pain."

And then … Peppar leaned down and pulled the plug from the fan. And he winked.

"One does what one must. Take care, boy."

I was going to call for the guard, call my lawyer, tell them about Peppar, get a new trial …

But what would be the point? I had committed murder, and I was being punished, albeit not for the murder I committed. Such is the fate of a generation raised on irony.

My last request is to wear black tie.

I tell my keepers: "My wife always said one should wear black tie for formal occasions. I should think an execution would qualify … "

As I sit here and wait … I realize … I am no one's boyfriend anymore. No one's son-in-law. No one's husband.

I am a murderer. And that will have to do.

MARGARET FAYDLE COMES TO TOWN

LUCY. I am a murderer. Well. Will be. Soon. That's a promise. Bob says I never stick to my guns, not even my figurative guns, but then Bob's a stickler, and I'm not. His name's Bob Stickler, after all. My name's Stickler too, but a Stickler by marriage is not the same thing. This time my gun's good and stuck.

It began when Margaret Faydle came to town. I should say Margaret Morrison Faydle Haverland Keith Sprechne Faydle Faydle. Which tells you something about Margaret's marital history. After her husbands would die or divorce her, she never ended up rich enough to take it easy. But she'd always end up on her feet and in very nice shoes.

Hadn't seen in her in a nun's age. And then one day … Margaret Faydle comes to town.

This was six weeks ago.

Standing at the corner outside the Members' Center next to Janet MacPherson and her new hip. I'd just come out of the pharmacy, with my pills and Bob's. What I see first is the hat. Ever since I knew her it was hats. When we were in school back home, it'd be some Saturday afternoon downtown, and there she'd be coming out of The Hub with something just in from Chicago or New York. She'd seen it on Rosalind Russell or Carole Lombard, and next thing you know it was on Margaret's head. Her father didn't have a lot of money either. I think that family went without food to keep that bitch in hats.

Margaret wore hats all through the forties and fifties, like we all did, but when we stopped wearing them, she didn't. At first we thought that was strange or maybe she'd gone bald, but she knew better. It preserved her in the time the men she went after remembered as their best years — when a woman with a hat was just who they wanted and maybe couldn't quite get.

Standing outside the pharmacy with Janet MacPherson — who is not well by the way — I saw it. The hat. A sharp little flash of blue, at that angle. My heart skipped. I didn't want to look lower, but I had to. Below the blue hat, below the blue brim was the same pale brow and the pencil eyebrows and the red gash — goddammit Jesus persnickety Christ!

I knew she wasn't visiting. Visitors go right through the main gates to whoever they're seeing. No, Margaret was walking into the offices of Mr. Finn and that nice Ms. Lupino. They show the units. And Margaret had luggage. That meant only one thing: Margaret Faydle was moving in.

I tried not to show my true feelings. I didn't want Janet to know. And then I turned and looked at her. Janet had gone white. And I knew then: Margaret had screwed Janet's husband too.

Dinner at home that night. Bob and I are in one of the condos. The way things work at Riddle Key is the biggest units are the villas, they're detached, then the condos, we share a garage with the Kilmers from back home. Then the apartments. That's where you don't have more than a fridge and a zapper, and all your meals are down in the Coconut Room. Last is the senior center, the dump chute to death.

Bob and I were watching *Jeopardy*. Bob likes to play along, calling out, "I'll take Military Disasters for fifty!" I hadn't mentioned Margaret.

Last any of us had seen her was back home one summer right after she'd buried her last husband. I thought she might have come to the end of her time. She looked a little thinner — but then she was one of those gals who had one of those pillows that said, "You can never be too rich or too thin" and she'd taken some of the stuffing out of the pillow to make it thinner.

Bob was barking next to me, "What was the Battle of the Bulge?!"

I turned to him.

"Janet MacPherson and I were down near the New Members' Hut today after I picked up your pills and guess who we saw was moving in?"

The clue was "Winston Churchill said this famous line in Fulton, Missouri."

Bob didn't say a word. He squinted at the TV as if he was trying to think. Which is when I knew he knew Margaret was in town. He wasn't trying to answer the question, he was playing for time. I mean, even I knew the answer: This was a rerun.

"What is 'An Iron Curtain has descended?'"

That night, in bed, three in the morning, tossing and turning. It wasn't fair. Live seventy-eight years and you move all the way down to Florida to get away from the snow and cold and the bad memories, and then she has to come barging back in!

When I'd told Bob Margaret was moving in, he pretended to be surprised. Jesus, what a lousy actor! He even said, "Well, I'm very surprised!"

I didn't call him on it.

When it was new and raw, and they were going off to bonk like guppies in hotel rooms and her place and the back of the station wagon and that one time they used our house when I was in the hospital for the hysterectomy — which irked me, I must confess. I was in no mood for forgiving, even after it was over, after he said he'd realized his mistake and what could he do to make it up to me … hands clasped like Mary Pickford, on his knees in the rec room, his bad knees as he reminded me through his tears … only time I ever saw Bob cry was that night and the day I wrecked the Crown Victoria.

He said he'd ended it, and he was wrong and a fool and not worth my love and would I take him back…?

I did.

Of course I had believed him, believed him when I found out they were at the motel that last afternoon, May 9, 1975, that he had gone there to call it off, instead of the truth which was that she told him to meet her there so she could tell him she was dumping him to marry Lou Sprechne.

And I had to pretend he had chosen to come back to me.

Well, what do you do when you're forty-nine years old, no children, living in a mock Colonial near the lake?

I punished him. For a few years. We tried to avoid her at parties and places, but it's a small town, and frankly when you realize your husband is one of a team, it starts to get almost funny. The rest of us began to pick out the signs when Margaret was about to swoop onto one of the other husbands. Sometimes we'd try to warn the wronged wife, discreet little warnings like, "Margaret is fucking your husband."

By the time we hit sixty, things had teetered back to normal … by which I mean I was apologizing to Bob for not making dinner on time, and not picking up the pills, and not being interesting enough to require his love or devotion and fidelity.

And this is how things were for us that night, at three A.M. the day Margaret Faydle came to Riddle Key. Me awake in the bed, wondering why my life had come to this.

And Bob awake in the room next to me … wondering what, I wondered.

The invitation came the next day. Cocktails at six. A welcoming party for Margaret Faydle thrown by … Margaret Faydle.

I was at Dr. Nagangupta's office to get the results of my tests, and Janet had all the dirt: Margaret was staying in Ted Varner's villa just six circles away. Ted and Sheila Varner had lived there until Sheila died last spring and then when Ted broke his back coming out of the Tiki Hut six weeks ago they'd moved him straight to the senior center, but he hadn't given up his villa. Ted's certain he's going to move back, but everybody knows no one comes back from the senior center.

Apparently Margaret heard the villa was empty and called Ted, said she was looking for a place to stay the winter, boo-hoo, and one-two-three, here she is. And now she's throwing her own welcoming party, using Ted's charge cards.

And we're invited. Well, everybody's invited. Not just the men she slept with and the women she ruined.

I go into Dr. Nagangupta, look at the tests, sigh at the results, discuss the follow-up, the new prescriptions.

I'm supposed to take my X-rays into St. Petersburg to see the new specialist, but I stop when I see her. My hand on the handle of the car, there she is, in a golf cart — she doesn't golf, everyone has golf carts down here — Margaret, whizzing by with a hat on at a jaunty angle, a cigarette stabbing up into the air like a sex-change Roosevelt.

And Bob in the seat next to her. His golf hat blows off. Bob makes a grab for it, but it's gone. Margaret laughs. They both laugh. And the golf cart zooms off through a row of forsythia.

That night. Bob's late when he comes in. He kisses me on the forehead, sits close, on the ottoman, how was the doctor, what did he say? I say fine.

His bald head is burned. His bald head, which has made him fear skin cancer since the age of thirty-six, on which he smears three kinds of sunscreen with an SPF of 198, this before he puts on his hat, is burnt to a crisp.

"You're red," I say.

"A little." Bob is sanguine about his head and the carcinoma that is steadily brightening over it.

"Where's your hat?"

"Lost it."

Bob is relaxed about the loss of his hat, his favorite hat, the hat he got when he and the fellas won the Riddle Skins Senior two years before. Bob gets angry if he loses a pack of matches from the WinnDixie, but today he could care less if he lost his favorite first place trophy hat.

I show him the invitation. His brow furrows, red and white grooves as he pretends not to know about the cocktail party.

"Should we go?" he asks. "It's up to you," he says. "Would you be comfortable?" He takes my hand, he's very solicitous, he's like Marcus Welby.

I say "no."

He nods. Nods again. He wants to go, the bastard.

"Okay," he says. "We won't. We'll be the only ones though. That'll stick out."

Bob goes into the kitchen to take his pills.

I call to him: "All right, we'll go. But we won't stay long."

Bob is ecstatic. But he shakes his head.

"No, really, if it's uncomfortable, if it makes you feel inhibited or shy … "

Note the problem: It's not that she stole my husband from me then threw him back like a dead fish, it's that I'm too intimidated by her blazing light to be in the room with her!

"No." I say. "We're going."

Bob sighs, pops a beta blocker. "If you say so," he says.

Tom Sawyer thinks he's made the dumb girl paint another fence.

And all the time I know his golf hat is under the cushion of my La-Z-Boy.

Night of the cocktail party. For the last three days every married woman in Riddle Key has spent her every waking hour in front of mirrors. Like the German army, Margaret Faydle makes her opponents rise to the occasion.

We pull into Ted's circle. Lots of golf carts. We still drive a car, but pretty much everyone else is using golf carts. Margaret has hired some Cuban valet boys. They use cars to drive them to where they park the golf carts.

The villa is filled. Everybody from back home is there. That's one of the strangest things you learn when you retire to Florida. You all move down in a group, only now we're tanned like a purse and can't remember our names.

I get a drink. A Brandy Alexander without the brandy. I like the brandy, but the brandy does not like me.

I go through the den to the deck …

And there she is. At a table near the balcony, surrounded by as many men as are alive and ambulatory.

Bob stands apart, holding a martini — neither Bob nor I drink martinis. Bob has a look on his face as he watches Margaret with her other beaus. It's a look I've never seen on Bob before but I recognize it. It's jealousy.

We don't talk about it during the drive home, the three-minute-drive home that we could have walked when we were young. We don't talk about it that night.

And then, it's a Tuesday.

I'm in St. Petersburg, at the doctor's office, in the waiting room. There are two gals across the coffee table from me. They don't recognize me, but I know they live over at Sunset Point. I pretend to leaf through an AARP brochure. They're talking about someone.

"They say she moved down when she got wind one of her old beaus has a wife who's on her last legs, and she's just waiting for the day she kicks it."

I don't wait for my results.

I get into the car and drive back to Riddle Key.

I want to see Bob, the Bob who wooed me, loved me, stood with me in front of God and my family and my friends and made promises to last a lifetime.

I stop at the drug store for my prescription — I'm having palpitations — and as I'm about to leave, the druggist, the snarky one, the one who looks like a weasel, says —

"Uh-oh. One more."

He turns and fishes around for a bottle.

"Just got the call. Lucky you came by."

He hands me the bag and smiles a greasy grin.

"Have a good night."

I go out into the sun, into the car, up the drive, inside the house. I open the bag and look at the bottle.

The name: Robert Stickler. The prescription: Viagra …

I begin planning the murder the next day.

I went to the pharmacist first. Andrew, the young one. He's so sweet. And confused. I tell him the prescription I got the day before didn't have my Valluturinal in it. He seems surprised, but he believes me, and he refills it.

When he goes to lunch, I go back and see Misty, the one with the funny eye. "The prescription I got from Andrew didn't have my Valluturinal." She's an idiot, so she believes me too.

I do the same thing at the St. Petersburg Eckerd's and the Clearwater Rexall, three times each. By the end of the day I have enough Valluturinal to kill everyone in the state of Florida.

I go home. It's *Jeopardy* time. But Bob is out. Bob is out all the time now. He's volunteering, he says. He's a Big Brother or a Fat Grandpa or whatever the hell he's pretending to be. But I know he's slipping from yard to yard until he gets to Margaret's villa.

He has hidden his Viagra. He puts it in his golf bag, down in the sack where he keeps his balls. Two pills a day. I switch them for Ex-Lax.

When I retrieve the mail that day I see there's a dance at the club Saturday night. Saturday will be perfect.

Now I always study the backs of my prescriptions. I know what to take on an empty stomach, what to take with food, how much water, and not to drive a tractor when I'm doing it.

The Bob part will be easy. We share a medicine cabinet.

But Margaret will be difficult.

For the next three days I'm on a tight schedule.

Wednesday I go in for my weekly appointment with Dr. Nagangupta. When it's nearly done, I ask him: "And how are those kids of yours?" And as he turns to dig out his wallet, I peel off three prescription sheets from his pad and pocket them before he faces me again.

That afternoon, when Bob's back from another bout of his newfound social conscience, he finds me in bed. I tell him I need my pills, but I forgot to get my prescriptions filled, can he go down to the pharmacy…?

Usually Bob would berate me for being so unorganized, but the trip will give him a chance to drop by Margaret's. I give him three prescriptions: my forgeries of Dr. Nagangupta's signature on every one.

Thursday I go into St. Petersburg with Janet to buy a dress. It costs three thousand dollars of Bob's money. And it's worth it.

Back home, I check to see if Bob is watching TV. No. He's left me a note. He's doing craft work with some underprivileged Seminole children.

It's Friday, the day before the dance. I call Margaret Faydle.

"Hullo?" That fake English accent she stole from Greer Garson in *Mrs. Miniver.*

"Why, Lucy. I'm so sorry we didn't get a chance to chat the other night!"

"Me, too!" I say in my sparky housewife voice. We gals know how to make up for our lack of innate interest by overcompensating in the Doris Day department.

"That's why I was wondering. What if I dropped over tomorrow noon!"

"Why, that would be swell," Margaret coos. She uses words like swell and nifty. The sporty old slut.

Saturday, I'm up early. Bob is in, watching The History Channel. *Great Traitors.*

"Not out with the NAACP today, dear? No street kids to teach English to?"

"Er ... no. They're, uh, they're under house arrest for the weekend."

The bastard. He knows I'm having lunch with Margaret, so he's got nowhere to go.

I say goodbye to Bob. He doesn't notice. He's entranced by the voice of Roger Mudd and the face of Alger Hiss.

When Margaret opens the door, she is a sight to behold in a 1950s thing, all camel and cream. And yet it's not out of style. Nothing on Margaret ever goes out of style.

"My dear one!" Peck peck, each cheek. "Do, do come in."

And I do.

It's quiet when she shuts the door. Just the sound of the sun outside.

"Here," she purrs, "come through. Drink? No, don't tell me. Brandy Alexander without the brandy! Such a little lady's drink."

"What're you having," I ask?

"Gin martini, bourbon back."

"Make it two."

Margaret's eyes widen. I recall she was the first gal back home to wear contact lenses. Half the wives she cuckolded found out they were being cheated on when they found little round glass things in their husband's boxer shorts.

When we've sat down — she's made mine a triple, to see if I'll throw up — we talk about this and that, about the cocktail party, about the dance that night.

Finally the time has come. I stand.

"What's the matter, dear? Drink too strong?"

I have been careful with the drink. But I pretend otherwise.

"I should have checked my medication. May I use your powder room?"

"Of course, petal."

And I run to the hall. Run, so she will be discouraged from following me.

As I pass the bedroom, I take out Bob's Senior Skins hat and toss it under the bed with one swift swish, like I'm Oddjob from *Goldfinger*.

I go into the bathroom. I run the water. I've only got a minute or two before she comes knocking to see if my head's in the toilet.

I open her medicine cabinet. Margaret doesn't have the kind of medications I have. Just four rows of diet pills.

I only need one. I choose it, careful not to smear her prints.

Knock, knock. "How are we doing. Dear?"

I put Margaret's bottle into my purse, flush the toilet, take off my watch and drop it under the paper roll.

I open the door.

"All done."

I say, "I'd better be going, lie down for a while before the dance." She does not try to stop me.

As I leave the villa, I break down and cry.

The Cuban gardeners try not to notice, but when I am sure I have my witnesses, I get into my car and go home. I make sure no one sees me drop the spare key in the flower pot. I go inside and lock the door.

The phone is ringing. Margaret has found the watch.

"Dear one, you silly, you left your absolutely charming timepiece in my powder room. Shall I bring it to the dance tonight?"

"Oh, dear," I say, "Do you think you could bring it over to the house?"

"Now?"

"Do you mind too terribly?"

I can hear the furious sigh, but she says yes.

"If I'm in the bath, come in the side door, there's a key in the flower pot."

She's on her way! As Margaret pulls her golf cart into the driveway I call Janet across the street. I whisper, like I'm hiding in the closet.

"Janet, someone's trying to get into my house!"

"Lemme see," she grumbles. I see Janet lumber to her front window and stare across the street. "It's goddamn Margaret Faydle! She's taking some key from the flower pot."

Why, I don't leave a key in the flower pot!

"Well, she's inside now, so you better get ready to hit her with a frying pan."

I click off. I hear Margaret slap down the watch on the kitchen counter, and leave.

I take a bath. A long one, the oils and salts. I take a long time dressing, my make-up, my hair.

When I pass his room, Bob is struggling into his tux. Actually it's not such a struggle anymore. He's lost weight. He's keeping fit. All that basketball he's playing with the Special Olympics Team.

We drive together to the club.

Inside, Bob looks over my shoulder, to find her, no doubt.

I go to the bar where Dr. Nagangupta is standing.

And how are you doing tonight, Mrs. Stickler?

"I'm a little woozy. All those pills Bob said you want me to take."

"Woozy?" He looks perplexed.

"The pills Bob said you prescribed. You sure do have me taking a ton!"

Dr. Nagangupta furrows his brow. "But I have not prescribed a ton of pills."

"Oh! Excuse me," I say, and move away from the good and honest doctor, leaving him with his perplexing thought.

In a corner, Janet is nursing a vat of vodka.

"Hey, how'd things go with Margaret?"

"Well, she seemed very surprised when I came out of the bedroom. She said she wanted to drop off something, but when I pressed her she couldn't tell me what it was."

"What about the key?"

"Well, I asked her how she got in, and she said the door was unlocked."

"Lying bitch. I saw her take the key. Well, if you didn't leave the key, who did?"

And I leave Janet, my faithful friend with the dark suspicion that will linger in her mind.

I go to Bob.

Bob's watching Margaret in the center of another swarm of men, but he's pretending to talk wetlands policy with Mort Hoberman. Mort is pro wetlands, Bob is for a state made of asphalt.

"Bob. I'm … I'm not doing too good."

"What is it?"

"I don't know. Could you take me home?"

Bob goes red. He has just seen an entire evening of thermometers and cold compresses flash before him.

"You don't have to stay with me. Just get me home, and you can come back."

"No, honey, I should stay with you."

Note the "should."

At home, I assure my husband of forty-seven years that I feel better. That it was just the heat and the crowd and my condition, which Dr. Nagangupta and the specialists have said doesn't get better.

Bob smiles down on me with a look of what looks like love and sympathy. Then he steals a glance at his watch.

"Go back to the dance, dear. Have fun."

Bob leans in, pecks my cheek.

And he's gone.

It's very quiet now.

I sit at my dressing table. I take the pill bottle I stole from Margaret's medicine cabinet and stick one of my little Valluturinal labels on it. And then I open the rest of the bottles. There are nine of them. A lot to take. But I have plenty of water.

After I'm done, I will put the empty pill bottles in the trash.

And when they find my body they will think it was by natural causes. I was very ill, after all, everyone knew that. But they thought I had more time.

And then Dr. Nagangupta will remember what I said about Bob giving me more pills than he had prescribed. And fearing a wrongful death suit, he will order an autopsy, where they'll find my stomach full of poison.

And then the pharmacy will retrieve the forged prescription slips written with Bob's pen and taken in by Bob not long before I died.

And the pill bottles will be found. One of them with Margaret's fingerprints on it — the bottle I took from her own medicine cabinet.

And Janet will recall Margaret sneaking into my house with a key left there by someone who was not me.

And Bob's hat will be found under Margaret's bed.

And the gardeners will recall my weeping.

And Bob and Margaret will be arrested for my murder. And in this state, they will fry.

So. I am a murderer. Will be. Soon as the pills take hold.

Oh, I know they might not get the chair. Old people, after all. But old people go fast in prison.

Margaret taking showers with all those "nice" girls in the diesel joint.

And Bob becoming the bitch of a three-time loser named Baby Lard.

It's not perfect justice. But then … I'm not a stickler.

MATCH WITS WITH MINKA LUPINO

MINKA. I am a murderer. Many times over. I do not like the term "serial killer," which, to my mind, suggests an emphasis on the numerical followed by too much time spent on the interstate highway system. My murders all took place in one locality.

Now, I should say right here at the beginning, I am not ashamed of having committed murder. You see, I believe in what is right. In justice. And every murder I ever planned — save one — was planned in that spirit of rightness, fairness and justice, the kind of murder planning that I like to think our forefathers would have approved of.

Besides, I was not always a murderer. Murderers are not born that way. The works of Jay G. Garland have taught me that. Jay G. Garland is my favorite author, the greatest mystery writer of all time, whose detective, gay Broadway impresario Jolly St. Holly, is always stumbling onto murders along the Great White Way. Jay G. Garland is the author of *Murder with the Lunts*, *Murder with Carol Channing*, and his magnum opus, *Murder with the Cast of A Chorus Line at Sardi's After the Show.*

He taught me that murderers have their reasons — usually splashy and interesting reasons with a lot of diabolical planning that is nonetheless foiled when Jolly sees through their one big mistake.

Not that Jay G. Garland is limited to his Broadway milieu. Under his pseudonym, "Maevis Marvella Pearl," he writes about Sister Angelicadore, the blind lesbian novice who solves convent crimes in sixteenth-century Venice; as well as his hard-core police procedurals written under the apt *nom de plume,* "Peter Dick Johnson."

I've been reading this man since I was in high school. And the day he came down to live at the Riddle Key Luxury Senior Retirement Living Center and Golf Course … well, you can imagine.

I wanted to tell him how exciting it was he was taking one of the new villas, how I was such a fan, how whenever there was a lull in the Members' Office and Mr. Finn was out showing a prospective couple around, I'd sneak out a copy of *Pippin Must Die* or *Nine Novenas to Death* or *Cock My Gun Slowly.*

All in paperback of course. I can't afford the hardback copies.

But I never said a word to him. For someone of his stature, Mr. Finn handled all of the details himself. I'd never even heard Mr. Garland's voice over the phone.

At least that's the way it was before. Before I ever thought I'd meet him. Before I became … a murderer.

It started with Mrs. Moses. Her name wasn't Mrs. Moses, of course. I was the only one who called her Mrs. Moses, and just to myself.

Her real name was Mrs. Westland from Sherrodsville, Pennsylvania. And she became Mrs. Moses to me because when I met her, she talked on and on about how her son and his wife had adopted a little Korean baby, and for the longest time she'd never been allowed to visit. Never seen her own grandson, just seen his pictures.

Mrs. Westland would say, "And I just felt like Moses in the Promised Land, yes, I did, I thought I'd never see that little baby, I was just like Moses in the Promised Land, just like him, just like Moses looking down on the land he was promised but he knew he'd never see, just like Moses!"

The reason she hadn't seen the baby was because she was in a war with her son and his wife. They wanted her to move down to Florida, where they could quote look after her, unquote, which is code for, "We don't want to have to fly up to that hick town in Pennsylvania anymore to make sure you aren't dead or eating cat food."

Mrs. Moses didn't want to move to Florida, of course, she liked it in that hick town, that's where her friends were, that's where she'd met her husband Phil, that's where Phil was buried. And Phil had left her well-off, so she could afford help if she needed it, thank you very much, and was not interested in becoming part of any old folk's home.

Well, Mrs. Moses' only son, Young Phil and his wife Suzy didn't see it that way. And so, when they adopted the baby, known as Young-Young Phil, they said, "You can't come down to see him, unless you agree to at least LOOK at Riddle Key."

So there was a stand-off. And it lasted eight months, which is a long time for an eighty-four-year-old woman and this is your only grandchild.

"Why it's like Moses in the … "

So she gave in. Just a visit. After all, she'd get to see that grandchild of hers. She'd even ordered him a Korean War G.I. Joe doll, not quite understanding that it didn't mean the doll was Korean.

When Mrs. Moses came through the gates, she didn't know what hit her. The idea was they'd bring her in to "take a look" at the facilities — the restaurants, the shops, the pharmacy, the clinic, the basement storage rooms with hurricane protection — then, at the end of the visit, they'd take her up to a sample villa, just for a peek, go inside … and there would be her whole life from back home, hijacked, shipped by Mayflower, and plopped down where it was more convenient for THEM.

I was there when they showed her the villa — how nicely her breakfront fit the dining room, how well the upright piano looked near the window …

Mrs. Moses wanted to bolt right back to Sherrodsville, of course, but it was too late. Why, Young Phil had already done all that work, the expense of moving things, closing up the house, having her stocks and bank accounts reassigned to his power of attorney. And him not the success in wholesale scuba gear that his father had been in coal.

She moved in that night. She'd put up her pictures of Young-Young on the living room wall, make some new friends, make the best of it.

She was dead three months later.

Young Phil and his wife were on vacation in Bermuda with Young Phil's new investment pals when I called them with the news.

Phil said: "Geez, we're only two days into our vacation, would you mind putting Mom on ice for a week 'til we get back? I mean, she'll keep, right?"

I checked Mrs. Moses' living will, her special requests, what she wanted to be buried with — wedding ring, yes, engagement ring, no — she wanted to be buried next to her husband back in Sherrodsville, so when Young Phil and Suzy came into the office — Young-Young was with the new nanny — I assumed it was to arrange transport up north.

"Cremation," Young Phil said. "You do that here on the grounds, right?"

" … Yes … "

"Well," he said, "let's do that!"

"But the request here says … "

Mr. Finn cleared his throat.

"I believe the crematorium is available at five, Ms. Lupino.

Friday is never very busy."

I tried not to show my reaction. "As for the service," I said —

"No service," said Suzy. "She didn't have any friends here anyway."

I nodded. Very professional. "Will you be coming by to pick up the cremains?"

"No," said Young Phil. "Just … " And he made a gesture — *(Does flip-wrist gesture.)* — that either meant "whisk it away" or "I'm really effeminate."

Mr. Finn stepped in. "Ms. Lupino will take you to the storage room where your mother's things have been preserved. Anything of value we can ship."

I take them across the lot to the storage rooms, a big cement block set three stories into the mud. It's brand-new — not fully open yet — the cooling and ventilation system isn't even working.

We reach Mrs. Moses' room. I unlock the door. Suzy turns to me. "You may go, Miss Lupino."

I nod, servile, eyes downcast.

I leave the room, filled with old furniture and pictures of what I'm sure Mrs. Moses would have called her "loved ones."

But I do not go away. I stand just outside the door. And listen.

"Well, she went faster than I thought," says the bereaved daughter-in-law.

"Not fast enough," replies the loving son. "Two years ago, the portfolio would have been worth a quarter more and I coulda bought six more waterfront lots."

"Can we use any of this crap?" asks his blushing bride.

"Nah. Cheap veneer and naugahyde."

Suzy is getting all soft: "Shouldn't we save some of these things for Young-Young?"

"What're we gonna give him, this needlepoint sign that says "With God All Things Are Possible?" Bad enough he's got that kimchee G.I. Joe thing."

I move closer to the door. The edges have rubber seals.

I take a moment and recall all the Mrs. Moseses I've seen, hustled into a beige wall-to-wall coffin at twelve hundred a month. All the sons and daughters who've asked Mr. Finn, "How long, on average, do they last once they're in here?" The grandkids who have to be bribed to visit, give Grandma a kiss, pretend not to look bored and sullen while they watch their parents do to their grandparents what they'll do to their parents some day.

Inside, I hear Young Phil:

"Hey, look, my Cub Scouts cap — "

The door makes no sound, just a whisper of a pneumatic whoosh.

I don't hear the pounding until I'm well up the steel stairs to the floor above.

When I meet Mr. Finn at the crematorium, I tell him the family wanted some time with the mementos of their loss.

"No skin off my honker," he says, wittily. "See you Monday."

Monday is, of course, not much fun. One of the Cuban fellas who's supposed to clear out the room finds the bodies. He says the couple was found hugging a needlepoint sign that read "With God All Things Are Possible." Even though it's impossible to open the door.

The bodies are buried in Sherrodsville, Pennsylvania, which I think is a nifty touch. The money will eventually snake its way to Young-Young, who is adopted again, this time by a Korean couple. They name him Kevin.

Did I feel guilty? No.

Did I feel good? No. But I felt just.

I didn't kill again for almost a year.

Mr. James was a favorite of mine. When he and his wife had moved into an efficiency apartment — no fancy villas or condos for him — he'd made a point of dropping by the Members' Office a couple times a day.

One day he dropped in and asked to see some information on deep-sea fishing and as I handed him the brochures he bit my arm. And left his teeth there.

"What are you doing?!"

"You've heard of Jaws? I'm Jaws."

I kept his teeth for the rest of the day and after that we got on fine.

That year Mrs. James went through a couple of nurses — one was too young, one was too fat, one was a Holy Roller who was always trying to get them to donate money to her "tabernacle," which I think was run out of the back of her Dodge Dart. Finally they settled on Muff.

Muffalda was her real name, and she was the type of woman who had not given up on capri pants long past her legs' sell-by date. She had Bozo the Clown red hair and a nose the size of my head.

But Mr. James liked her. And Mrs. James … well, by that time, it was hard to tell what Mrs. James liked or didn't like, and two months after Muff was hired, Mrs. James was dead.

After the burial, Mr. James' daughters figured their father would let Muff go. But Mr. James, who had been independent all his life, decided he needed someone now. His eyesight, his walk, the lonely nights …

The daughters were not pleased. Especially when they couldn't find some of the jewelry their mother had promised them. Nor were they pleased when they saw the way Muff joked with Mr. James and tickled him while they watched *Diagnosis: Murder*. They particularly didn't like it when Mr. James decided to renegotiate his contract with Mr. Finn and move from his one-bedroom efficiency apartment to a two-bedroom condo with all the amenities.

"You wouldn't spend that much on Mother!" the daughters spat.

And they were right. They were also right that he didn't buy his late wife a new Cadillac, or new clothes or any of the other accessories Muff seemed to grow once she and Mr. James were ensconced in the expensively redecorated condo.

I hadn't seen Mr. James in a while. He'd stopped dropping by the way he used to, and one night I was at the Applebee's on Route 19, after work, having a Cherry Herring at the bar when who walks in but Muff. She sees me and smiles, sidles onto the barstool next to me.

"Fancy seein' you here," she barks. She sounds like Rose Marie after having swallowed a cheese grater. "Gimme a boilermaker!"

"Night off?" I ask.

"Sorta. The old guy was wearin' me out so … "

She takes out a prescription bottle from her purse.

" … I popped a couple Valium into his Metamucil. He'll be out for the night. He thinks he's such an old bull … let me tell you: I'm breakin' my wrist just to hoist the weenie!"

Muff downs her boilermaker. I notice she's wearing a diamond wristwatch.

"That's a pretty watch," I say.

"Got it from Mrs. James." She coughs up some tobacco phlegm to make her even prettier.

"Fell off her wrist as the chill set in."

Now, I do not know what it is that makes people like Muff want to confide in me, but I do not disabuse them of this misplaced trust.

For the next three hours, she regales me with tales of tricking Mr. James out of money, out of jewelry, and how a lawyer is coming next week to look at Mr. James' old will that really needs to be rewritten.

"He can't live forever," she snorts. "Not with the workouts I'm givin' him."

By midnight, Muff is pretty drunk. Slathering on her orange lipstick she confides she came to Applebee's to get laid, but I note there are no blind penitentiary escapees to be had. Besides, she has to go back to Mr. James.

"There's his sheets gotta go in the dryer. And I hafta make sure he's still breathing."

She slips off her stool right to the floor.

"You're in no shape to drive," I say.

Which is true, I've pumped her boilermakers with the contents of her Valium bottle for three hours now.

I drive her back to Riddle Key in the Cadillac, use her key card to go through the gates. I get her into the condo. No one sees.

Mr. James is dead to the world, snoring the way a seventy-nine-year-old man on sleeping pills snores.

Muff stumbles into the utility room and leans over the clothes washer …

"Gotta get these sheets in the dryer or they'll mildew … "

Which are her last words, unless you count, "Hey!"

— As I swing the full bottle of Heavy Duty Economy Size Tide at her head.

Once she's out, I take the wet sheets and make sure they're caught tight on the steel tumbler. Then I take the other wet end and tie it around Muff's neck.

Set to spin. And push.

I regret the shock to Mr. James when he finds her, but I know I've made the right decision when he moves back the next week to his old efficiency apartment, and his round-the-clock care is a two-hundred-and-fifty-pound Samoan man named Tondaleyo.

I'd like to say that was the end of my murder spree. But after you've done it once or twice, it just gets easier and easier. Like bicycle riding or sex, which to me is the same thing.

After Muff was Mr. Dofferman, the undertaker who liked to take things off the deceased before the family got there.

And then there was Officer Getz, who arrested the seniors on trumped-up driving infractions and threatened them with losing their licenses unless they gave him half their Social Security checks every month.

And Nurse Vigesmond, and the Manzano brothers of Manzano Bros. Construction, and the check-out girl at the Holiday Inn. All the ones who took advantage and knew they shouldn't have.

And then … last week …

Mr. Finn comes into the office. And smiles. I know that smile. It's the smile Mr. Finn has when he's found a couple on their last legs and he's gotten them to sign a five-year fully loaded deluxe package lease he knows they're never gonna live long enough to enjoy. It's the smile he has when he's tricked the Cuban boys to work another hour because he didn't tell them about daylight savings. Mr. Finn is smiling that smile at me.

"Hi, there, killer."

I pretend I think he's come up with a clever nickname for me.

But he hasn't. He has a letter in his hand. And reads.

"There is a murderer among us. A murderer who has committed at least six killings in the last four years. And that murderer spends each working hour within the Members' Office of Riddle Key."

I swallow. "That's it?"

"Isn't that enough? I'm not saying I NEVER suspected you. I mean, the way Dr. Vasquez and his girlfriend got fried in that sitz bath. And when the Reverend Chuck got drowned during Mrs. Peshke's "Jesus Loves Jews" baptism? I've been looking through the files all weekend: suffocations, electrocutions … strangulation by sheets?! And one constant factor: Miss Minka Lupino."

I am sweating. I have killed so many people for such a long time now without fearing anyone that it is the mere newness of the concept that frightens me.

"Are you going to call the police?"

"And ruin a winning streak? No, Miss Lupino. I don't know who sent this, but I am afraid this office has overlooked your talents for too long. I want you to keep doing what you're doing. But with some guidance. We have a problem the front office is concerned about. As you know, our five-year plan almost always works to our advantage. But there is one who has overstayed his welcome, and due to a loophole in the original contract, is paying only the absolute minimum on a valuable villa that could garner millions on the open market … unless you kill him.

"His name is Jay G. Garland."

My heart has stopped.

"But he's my favorite author."

"Well, then, Minka ... this will give you a chance to meet him."

Three days later ...

It's Saturday night.

There's a dance up at the club. Big Band swing music drifts over the lawns as I drive the cart up the cul-de-sac to Mr. Garland's villa.

The plan is not mine, the plan is Mr. Finn's. I'm to ring the doorbell and tell Mr. Garland I have some documents for him to sign, and then hit him on the head with a lead pipe.

It's so pedestrian. Murdering a man like Jay G. Garland that way. It's like serving KFC to Julia Child.

When I reach the front steps, I halt.

There's music inside.

"You'll be swell.

"You'll be great.

"Gonna have the whole world on a plate."

I raise my hand to knock.

And the door opens.

Standing before me is a man of indeterminate age. His hair, what's left of it, is the color of squid ink and barbecue sauce. He has a mustache and goatee, half glasses, jowly cheeks, pale, he never goes out in the sun. He wears a green brocade dressing gown, a white dress shirt, and a dress bow tie. He holds a brandy snifter.

"Enter."

I go inside where I am immediately transported into a world that is the exact opposite of the world people who like sports inhabit. Red flock wallpaper, lamps with tassels, Persian carpets, antiques.

Jay G. Garland is limping, leaning on a cane with a huge ivory head shaped like snake.

"Have you ever noticed that women seldom get gout?"

I have noticed this, but this is not the time to brag.

I look at his foot. It's gigantic. A whole extra human at the end of his leg.

"Would you like a drink? What do we have? Vodka, brandy ... Cherry Herring?"

What did he say? No one offers anyone Cherry Herring.

"I can't touch the stuff. Dr. Nagangupta says if I do, my whole body will explode but I'll still have to hang around to clean up the mess. I'm a goddamned wreck, but they can't kill me. Sit. Now, before you do what you have to do, let me try out a story on you. You like mystery stories?"

Uh-huh.

"I've been noodling for a while, but I'm kinda rusty and I could use a sounding board. A killer. Let's call her a her. For fun. Starts to knock off the rotters in a town or village. They're stinkers and she's an avenging angel type. Gets in Dutch though, blackmailer has the goods on her, tells her she has to kill someone she doesn't have in the ledger, someone she likes … or the blackmailer gives her the shiv. This hooking you?"

Yeah, I'm hooked.

"Now. She could kill the blackmailer. But he's on his guard. So she has no choice but to go through with the deal. But she doesn't want to kill the guy. She'd like to put paid the blackmailer too. What's a girl to do?"

Jay G. Garland opens his hooded eyes.

"Question is — what kind of person is she? Is she a murderer? Really? In the sense that she is defined by her murder? A person who becomes a murderer and never really goes back to what she was kind of murderer? Or. Is she a very nice, very pleasant, very moral woman who *just happens to have committed a couple of murders?"*

"I think it's the latter."

"And frankly, she's pretty much run the table on all the creeps in the town, so there's no one left to bump off … save one."

He manages to lean forward, a big physical move. He makes Nero Wolfe look like Ben Vereen.

"Who do you think lets in all those bums anyway? Who turns a blind eye to the Young Phils and the Muffs and the rest of them?"

"The blackmailer?"

"Bingo. And by now … " He glances at a grandfather clock with the face of Noel Coward and I don't even want to tell you what the big hand and the little hand were. " … By now our friends should have him taken care of."

I stare at my idol.

"You're wondering how I knew it was you. Your last three murders were from my own books — *Murder Gotta Gimmick*, *A Little Night Murder* and *Murder at Jules Pfeiffer's Little Murders*. And who here at Riddle Key would know my books as well as Ms. Minka Lupino, who has purchased more cheesy paperback copies of my books than any other buyer on Amazon dot com."

I had left an e-trail!

"And now … since we understand each other … go."

"Go where?"

"To the club. There are people there who owe you a debt of gratitude. And they are waiting to show you their thanks."

So I go. As I do, I hear sirens. Two ambulances are shooting through the streets, one going up, one going down. Busy night in Riddle Key.

When I arrive at the club where Mr. Finn is to wait for me, the darkened ballroom is filled with figures, white hair, blue hair, toupees, bald pates … dancing in the dark to "Stardust." But there is no Mr. Finn.

I look down at the dance floor. There is a fine dusting of white sand on the parquet. And as I look at the dancers, I could swear I see the odd smile, hear the odd giggle, a whispered but buoyant "Shush!"

I look out through the ballroom windows to the eighteenth green. And there, gathered outside on the grass are … the Cuban fellas. They're sweating, glistening in the moonlight, as if they've been hard at work … and at this time of night …

They hold shovels and rakes. And they're smiling at me. And they give me a little thumbs-up good goin' sign.

Mr. Finn doesn't show up that night. Nor does he show up the next day or on Monday or any day at all, ever again.

These days Riddle Key is a lot less lethal a place. People die, that's part of the deal, but not at such an accelerated rate.

And out on the eighteenth green — where the Cuban boys buried Mr. Finn — the sand trap rides a little higher and a little lumpier.

Now I sit in Mr. Finn's old office, showing new tenants the grounds, the housing, the amenities. And they always notice the books on my shelf. All of them hardback first editions of the works of Jay G. Garland, all personally inscribed to me.

"To Minka Lupino. If anybody ever murdered me, I'd want it to be you."

End of Play

NEW PLAYS

★ **GUARDIANS by Peter Morris.** In this unflinching look at war, a disgraced American soldier discloses the truth about Abu Ghraib prison, and a clever English journalist reveals how he faked a similar story for the London tabloids. "Compelling, sympathetic and powerful." *–NY Times.* "Sends you into a state of moral turbulence." *–Sunday Times (UK).* "Nothing short of remarkable." *–Village Voice.* [1M, 1W] ISBN: 978-0-8222-2177-7

★ **BLUE DOOR by Tanya Barfield.** Three generations of men (all played by one actor), from slavery through Black Power, challenge Lewis, a tenured professor of mathematics, to embark on a journey combining past and present. "A teasing flare for words." *–Village Voice.* "Unfailingly thought-provoking." *–LA Times.* "The play moves with the speed and logic of a dream." *–Seattle Weekly.* [2M] ISBN: 978-0-8222-2209-5

★ **THE INTELLIGENT DESIGN OF JENNY CHOW by Rolin Jones.** This irreverent "techno-comedy" chronicles one brilliant woman's quest to determine her heritage and face her fears with the help of her astounding creation called Jenny Chow. "Boldly imagined." *–NY Times.* "Fantastical and funny." *–Variety.* "Harvests many laughs and finally a few tears." *–LA Times.* [3M, 3W] ISBN: 978-0-8222-2071-8

★ **SOUVENIR by Stephen Temperley.** Florence Foster Jenkins, a wealthy society eccentric, suffers under the delusion that she is a great coloratura soprano—when in fact the opposite is true. "Hilarious and deeply touching. Incredibly moving and breathtaking." *–NY Daily News.* "A sweet love letter of a play." *–NY Times.* "Wildly funny. Completely charming." *–Star-Ledger.* [1M, 1W] ISBN: 978-0-8222-2157-9

★ **ICE GLEN by Joan Ackermann.** In this touching period comedy, a beautiful poetess dwells in idyllic obscurity on a Berkshire estate with a band of unlikely cohorts. "A beautifully written story of nature and change." *–Talkin' Broadway.* "A lovely play which will leave you with a lot to think about." *–CurtainUp.* "Funny, moving and witty." *–Metroland (Boston).* [4M, 3W] ISBN: 978-0-8222-2175-3

★ **THE LAST DAYS OF JUDAS ISCARIOT by Stephen Adly Guirgis.** Set in a time-bending, darkly comic world between heaven and hell, this play reexamines the plight and fate of the New Testament's most infamous sinner. "An unforced eloquence that finds the poetry in lowdown street talk." *–NY Times.* "A real jaw-dropper." *–Variety.* "An extraordinary play." *–Guardian (UK).* [10M, 5W] ISBN: 978-0-8222-2082-4

NEW PLAYS

★ **THE GREAT AMERICAN TRAILER PARK MUSICAL music and lyrics by David Nehls, book by Betsy Kelso.** Pippi, a stripper on the run, has just moved into Armadillo Acres, wreaking havoc among the tenants of Florida's most exclusive trailer park. "Adultery, strippers, murderous ex-boyfriends, Costco and the Ice Capades. Undeniable fun." *–NY Post.* "Joyful and unashamedly vulgar." *–The New Yorker.* "Sparkles with treasure." *–New York Sun.* [2M, 5W] ISBN: 978-0-8222-2137-1

★ **MATCH by Stephen Belber.** When a young Seattle couple meet a prominent New York choreographer, they are led on a fraught journey that will change their lives forever. "Uproariously funny, deeply moving, enthralling theatre." *–NY Daily News.* "Prolific laughs and ear-to-ear smiles." *–NY Magazine.* [2M, 1W] ISBN: 978-0-8222-2020-6

★ **MR. MARMALADE by Noah Haidle.** Four-year-old Lucy's imaginary friend, Mr. Marmalade, doesn't have much time for her—not to mention he has a cocaine addiction and a penchant for pornography. "Alternately hilarious and heartbreaking." *–The New Yorker.* "A mature and accomplished play." *–LA Times.* "Scathingly observant comedy." *–Miami Herald.* [4M, 2W] ISBN: 978-0-8222-2142-5

★ **MOONLIGHT AND MAGNOLIAS by Ron Hutchinson.** Three men cloister themselves as they work tirelessly to reshape a screenplay that's just not working—*Gone with the Wind.* "Consumers of vintage Hollywood insider stories will eat up Hutchinson's diverting conjecture." *–Variety.* "A lot of fun." *–NY Post.* "A Hollywood dream-factory farce." *–Chicago Sun-Times.* [3M, 1W] ISBN: 978-0-8222-2084-8

★ **THE LEARNED LADIES OF PARK AVENUE by David Grimm, translated and freely adapted from Molière's *Les Femmes Savantes.*** Dicky wants to marry Betty, but her mother's plan is for Betty to wed a most pompous man. "A brave, brainy and barmy revision." *–Hartford Courant.* "A rare but welcome bird in contemporary theatre." *–New Haven Register.* "Roll over Cole Porter." *–Boston Globe.* [5M, 5W] ISBN: 978-0-8222-2135-7

★ **REGRETS ONLY by Paul Rudnick.** A sparkling comedy of Manhattan manners that explores the latest topics in marriage, friendships and squandered riches. "One of the funniest quip-meisters on the planet." *–NY Times.* "Precious moments of hilarity. Devastatingly accurate political and social satire." *–BackStage.* "Great fun." *–CurtainUp.* [3M, 3W] ISBN: 978-0-8222-2223-1

NEW PLAYS

★ **AFTER ASHLEY by Gina Gionfriddo.** A teenager is unwillingly thrust into the national spotlight when a family tragedy becomes talk-show fodder. "A work that virtually any audience would find accessible." *–NY Times.* "Deft characterization and caustic humor." *–NY Sun.* "A smart satirical drama." *–Variety.* [4M, 2W] ISBN: 978-0-8222-2099-2

★ **THE RUBY SUNRISE by Rinne Groff.** Twenty-five years after Ruby struggles to realize her dream of inventing the first television, her daughter faces similar battles of faith as she works to get Ruby's story told on network TV. "Measured and intelligent, optimistic yet clear-eyed." *–NY Magazine.* "Maintains an exciting sense of ingenuity." *–Village Voice.* "Sinuous theatrical flair." *–Broadway.com.* [3M, 4W] ISBN: 978-0-8222-2140-1

★ **MY NAME IS RACHEL CORRIE taken from the writings of Rachel Corrie, edited by Alan Rickman and Katharine Viner.** This solo piece tells the story of Rachel Corrie who was killed in Gaza by an Israeli bulldozer set to demolish a Palestinian home. "Heartbreaking urgency. An invigoratingly detailed portrait of a passionate idealist." *–NY Times.* "Deeply authentically human." *–USA Today.* "A stunning dramatization." *–CurtainUp.* [1W] ISBN: 978-0-8222-2222-4

★ **ALMOST, MAINE by John Cariani.** This charming midwinter night's dream of a play turns romantic clichés on their ear as it chronicles the painfully hilarious amorous adventures (and misadventures) of residents of a remote northern town that doesn't quite exist. "A whimsical approach to the joys and perils of romance." *–NY Times.* "Sweet, poignant and witty." *–NY Daily News.* "Aims for the heart by way of the funny bone." *–Star-Ledger.* [2M, 2W] ISBN: 978-0-8222-2156-2

★ **Mitch Albom's TUESDAYS WITH MORRIE by Jeffrey Hatcher and Mitch Albom, based on the book by Mitch Albom.** The true story of Brandeis University professor Morrie Schwartz and his relationship with his student Mitch Albom. "A touching, life-affirming, deeply emotional drama." *–NY Daily News.* "You'll laugh. You'll cry." *–Variety.* "Moving and powerful." *–NY Post.* [2M] ISBN: 978-0-8222-2188-3

★ **DOG SEES GOD: CONFESSIONS OF A TEENAGE BLOCKHEAD by Bert V. Royal.** An abused pianist and a pyromaniac ex-girlfriend contribute to the teen-angst of America's most hapless kid. "A welcome antidote to the notion that the *Peanuts* gang provides merely American cuteness." *–NY Times.* "Hysterically funny." *–NY Post.* "The *Peanuts* kids have finally come out of their shells." *–Time Out.* [4M, 4W] ISBN: 978-0-8222-2152-4

NEW PLAYS

★ **RABBIT HOLE by David Lindsay-Abaire.** Winner of the 2007 Pulitzer Prize. Becca and Howie Corbett have everything a couple could want until a life-shattering accident turns their world upside down. "An intensely emotional examination of grief, laced with wit." *–Variety.* "A transcendent and deeply affecting new play." *–Entertainment Weekly.* "Painstakingly beautiful." *–BackStage.* [2M, 3W] ISBN: 978-0-8222-2154-8

★ **DOUBT, A Parable by John Patrick Shanley.** Winner of the 2005 Pulitzer Prize and Tony Award. Sister Aloysius, a Bronx school principal, takes matters into her own hands when she suspects the young Father Flynn of improper relations with one of the male students. "All the elements come invigoratingly together like clockwork." *–Variety.* "Passionate, exquisite, important, engrossing." *–NY Newsday.* [1M, 3W] ISBN: 978-0-8222-2219-4

★ **THE PILLOWMAN by Martin McDonagh.** In an unnamed totalitarian state, an author of horrific children's stories discovers that someone has been making his stories come true. "A blindingly bright black comedy." *–NY Times.* "McDonagh's least forgiving, bravest play." *–Variety.* "Thoroughly startling and genuinely intimidating." *–Chicago Tribune.* [4M, 5 bit parts (2M, 1W, 1 boy, 1 girl)] ISBN: 978-0-8222-2100-5

★ **GREY GARDENS book by Doug Wright, music by Scott Frankel, lyrics by Michael Korie.** The hilarious and heartbreaking story of Big Edie and Little Edie Bouvier Beale, the eccentric aunt and cousin of Jacqueline Kennedy Onassis, once bright names on the social register who became East Hampton's most notorious recluses. "An experience no passionate theatergoer should miss." *–NY Times.* "A unique and unmissable musical." *–Rolling Stone.* [4M, 3W, 2 girls] ISBN: 978-0-8222-2181-4

★ **THE LITTLE DOG LAUGHED by Douglas Carter Beane.** Mitchell Green could make it big as the hot new leading man in Hollywood if Diane, his agent, could just keep him in the closet. "Devastatingly funny." *–NY Times.* "An out-and-out delight." *–NY Daily News.* "Full of wit and wisdom." *–NY Post.* [2M, 2W] ISBN: 978-0-8222-2226-2

★ **SHINING CITY by Conor McPherson.** A guilt-ridden man reaches out to a therapist after seeing the ghost of his recently deceased wife. "Haunting, inspired and glorious." *–NY Times.* "Simply breathtaking and astonishing." *–Time Out.* "A thoughtful, artful, absorbing new drama." *–Star-Ledger.* [3M, 1W] ISBN: 978-0-8222-2187-6